Mathematics

for **Key Stage Three**

The topic-based tests in this book are a brilliant way to stay on top of the KS3 Maths skills you'll need throughout Years 7-9 (ages 11-14) — and each one will only take up 10 minutes of your life!

This is **Book One**. It covers the **most straightforward material** from KS3 Maths, and revisits some of the most important skills from KS2. If you're looking for more challenging KS3 practice, Books Two and Three are also available.

10-Minute Tests
Book One

Contents

Geometry and Measures

Probability and Statistics

Published by CGP

Editors: Ceara Hayden, Sharon Keeley-Holden, Caley Simpson, Jonathan Wray

With thanks to Rosie Hanson and Shaun Harrogate for the proofreading.

ISBN: 978 1 78294 475 1

Printed by Elanders Ltd, Newcastle upon Tyne.
Clipart from Corel®

Based on the classic CGP style created by Richard Parsons

Number: Test 1

Give yourself **10 minutes** to do this test — there are **8 questions** to answer.

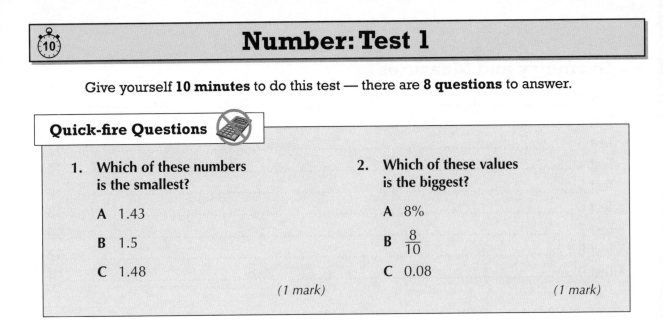

Quick-fire Questions

1. **Which of these numbers is the smallest?**

   A 1.43

   B 1.5

   C 1.48

   (1 mark)

2. **Which of these values is the biggest?**

   A 8%

   B $\frac{8}{10}$

   C 0.08

   (1 mark)

3. **Without using a calculator, fill in the boxes with the correct answer.**

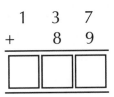

$$\begin{array}{ccc} 1 & 3 & 7 \\ + & 8 & 9 \\ \hline \Box & \Box & \Box \end{array}$$

(1 mark)

4. **Look at the numbers below.**

| 6 | 8 | 10 | 12 | 21 | 36 | 50 |

Write down the numbers from the box that are multiples of 3.

....

(1 mark)

Write down the numbers from the box that are factors of 24.

....

(1 mark)

5. **Barney has 272 coins. He shares them equally between 8 treasure chests.**

Without using a calculator, work out how many coins he puts in each chest.

....
(1 mark)

6. **Shilpa is knitting a scarf.**

9% of her scarf is red. Write this as a decimal.

....
(1 mark)

27% of her scarf is blue. What fraction of her scarf is **not** blue?

....
(1 mark)

7. **Round 7836 to 2 significant figures.**

....
(1 mark)

8. **Simplify $6^8 \times 6^2$ without using a calculator.**

Give your answer as a power of 6.

....
(1 mark)

Number: Test 2

Give yourself **10 minutes** to do this test — there are **8 questions** to answer.

Quick-fire Questions

1. Which of the following is correct?

   A $\frac{3}{5} = 0.6 = 60\%$

   B $\frac{1}{4} = 0.75 = 75\%$

   C $\frac{49}{50} = 0.49 = 49\%$

   (1 mark)

2. What is $\frac{32}{9}$ as a mixed number?

   A $3\frac{5}{9}$

   B $3\frac{2}{9}$

   C $3\frac{1}{3}$

   (1 mark)

3. The table shows the weights of four different vegetables in a giant vegetable competition.

Vegetable	Squash	Carrot	Parsnip	Beetroot
Weight (kg)	0.97	0.906	1.12	0.96

   Write down the vegetables in weight order, starting with the lightest.

   .... , ... , ... , ...
   (1 mark)

4. Pick two prices so that one is 100 times more than the other.

   | £6 | £47 | £65 | £407 | £470 | £650 | £6500 |

   £ .... and £ ....
   (1 mark)

5. A Maths book contains 270 questions. Camilla does 30 questions per day.

   Without using a calculator, work out how many days it takes her to complete the whole book.

   .... days
   (1 mark)

6. Work out $\frac{3}{4} + \frac{1}{6}$ without using a calculator.

Give your answer as a fraction in its simplest form.

....
(2 marks)

7. Calculate the rounding error when 7.69 is rounded to 1 decimal place.

....
(1 mark)

8. Use the information below to work out $\sqrt{169} + \sqrt{225}$.

| $13^2 = 169$ | $14^2 = 196$ | $15^2 = 225$ | $16^2 = 256$ |

....
(2 marks)

Score: | — / 10 |

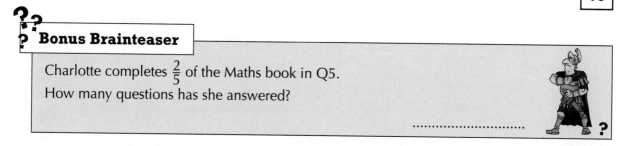

Bonus Brainteaser

Charlotte completes $\frac{2}{5}$ of the Maths book in Q5.
How many questions has she answered?

....

Number: Test 3

Give yourself **10 minutes** to do this test — there are **7 questions** to answer.

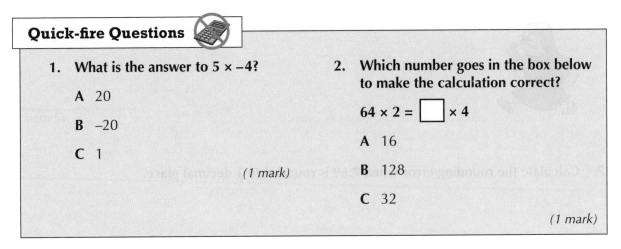

Quick-fire Questions

1. What is the answer to 5 × −4?

    A 20

    B −20

    C 1

    (1 mark)

2. Which number goes in the box below to make the calculation correct?

    64 × 2 = ☐ × 4

    A 16

    B 128

    C 32

    (1 mark)

3. Without using a calculator, fill in the boxes with the correct answer.

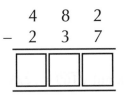

(1 mark)

4. Use two of the number cards below to make a prime number less than 50.

    6   **1**   **2**   **7**

    ....
    (1 mark)

Number: Test 3   6

5. **4600 cars drove through a set of traffic lights in one day.**

    1 in every 10 cars stopped at the traffic lights.
    How many cars was this?

    ....
    (1 mark)

    1 in every 100 cars went through when the lights were red.
    How many cars was this?

    ....
    (1 mark)

6. **Find the value of $10^3 - 10^2 - 10$ without using a calculator.**

    Give your answer as an ordinary number.

    ....
    (2 marks)

7. **Craig gets milk delivered every 3 days and Hannah gets milk delivered every 4 days.
    They both had milk delivered on 2nd June.**

    On which date will they next have milk delivered on the same day?

    ....
    (2 marks)

    Score: $\dfrac{\quad}{10}$

10

Give yourself **10 minutes** to do this test — there are **7 questions** to answer.

Quick-fire Questions

1. **What is 35 × 10?**

   A 3500

   B 3.5

   C 350

   (1 mark)

2. **What is 4300 ÷ 43?**

   A 10

   B 100

   C 1000

   (1 mark)

3. **List all the factors of 30.**

   ....

   (1 mark)

4. **Round 45.79 to 1 decimal place.**

   ....

   (1 mark)

5. **Use three of the numbers from the box below to make two equivalent proper fractions.**

   | 4 | 10 | 2 | 9 | 7 |

   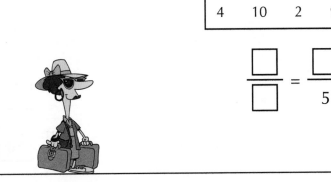

   $$\frac{\boxed{}}{\boxed{}} = \frac{\boxed{}}{5}$$

   (1 mark)

8

6. $2^8 = 256$

   Find 2^9 without using a calculator.

   ....
   (2 marks)

7. **The table below shows how much Sunny and Karmel get paid per hour for babysitting.**

	Pay per hour
Sunny	£6
Karmel	£7

   Karmel made £364 last year from babysitting.
   Without using a calculator, work out how many hours she babysat for.

   .... hours
   (1 mark)

   Sunny is saving up for a bike costing £212.
   Without using a calculator, work out how many whole hours he must babysit for to buy it.

   .... hours
   (2 marks)

   Score: $\dfrac{\quad}{10}$

Number: Test 5

Give yourself **10 minutes** to do this test — there are **6 questions** to answer.

3. **Sloe Island is one thousand, seven hundred and ten miles from Micaela's home.**

   Write this number in figures.

   ....
   (1 mark)

   The population of Sloe Island is about 29 750. Write this number in words.

   ....

   ....
   (1 mark)

4. **The table on the right shows how much it costs to go on the steam train.**

   Without using a calculator, work out the total fare for a senior and a child.

Steam Train Fares	
Adult	£8.75
Senior (65+)	£6.75
Child (under 16)	£3.50

   £ ....
   (1 mark)

5. **Work out the following, giving your answers as fractions in their simplest form.**

$\frac{5}{12} - \frac{1}{6}$

....
(1 mark)

$\frac{3}{8} \div \frac{2}{3}$

....
(1 mark)

6. **Without using a calculator, complete this factor tree to find the prime factors of 60.**

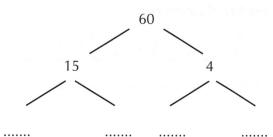

....   *(2 marks)*

Now write 60 as a product of its prime factors.

....
(1 mark)

Score: $\dfrac{}{10}$

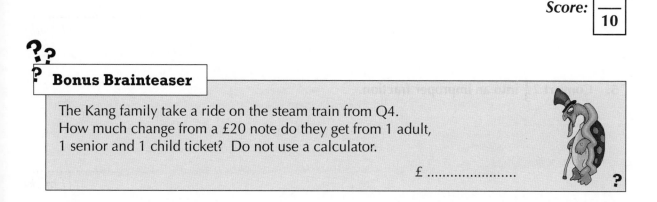

Bonus Brainteaser

The Kang family take a ride on the steam train from Q4.
How much change from a £20 note do they get from 1 adult,
1 senior and 1 child ticket? Do not use a calculator.

£ ....

Number: Test 6

Give yourself **10 minutes** to do this test — there are **8 questions** to answer.

Quick-fire Questions

1. **What is 6000 ÷ 100?**

    A 6

    B 60

    C 600

    (1 mark)

2. **2400 ÷ Δ = 240.**
    What does Δ equal?

    A 10

    B 100

    C 1000

    (1 mark)

3. **Atis has the following numbered counters.**

    What is the total value of all his odd-numbered counters?

    ....
    (1 mark)

4. **Find the lowest common multiple of 3 and 7.**

    ....
    (1 mark)

5. **Convert $2\frac{1}{3}$ into an improper fraction.**

    ....
    (1 mark)

12

6. **There are 30 students in Miss Smith's class. 18 of them are boys.**

   What percentage of her class are boys?

   .... %
   (1 mark)

7. **Estimate the answer to this calculation by rounding each number to 1 significant figure.**

   $$\frac{101.2 \div 3.9}{5.1}$$

   ....
   (2 marks)

8. **The formula $A = S^2$ is used to find the area of a square. A = area and S = side length.**

   If $S = 12$ cm, find the value of A.

   $A =$ .... cm^2
   (1 mark)

   If $A = 2456$ cm^2, find the value of S.
   Give your answer to 1 decimal place.

   $S =$ .... cm
   (1 mark)

   Score:
   $\frac{}{10}$

Number: Test 7

Give yourself **10 minutes** to do this test — there are **7 questions** to answer.

Quick-fire Questions

1. **Which of the following lists contains all prime numbers?**

   A 102, 111, 3

   B 5, 157, 99

   C 5, 11, 97

   (1 mark)

2. **What is the 5th prime number?**

   A 11

   B 9

   C 13

   (1 mark)

---

3. **Snowdon is 1085 m high and Scafell Pike is 978 m high.**

   Without using a calculator, find the difference in their heights.

   .... m

   (1 mark)

4. **Look at the following:**

   | A = 3.67 × 100 | | B = 0.037 × 1000 | | C = 0.307 × 10 000 |

   Which of the numbers A, B and C is the biggest?

   Biggest: ....

   (1 mark)

   Which of the numbers A, B and C is the smallest?

   Smallest: ....

   (1 mark)

14

5. **86 668 people attend a music festival.**

    Round this number to the nearest thousand.

    ....
    (1 mark)

6. **Zoe uses $\frac{3}{8}$ of a gallon of petrol on her drive to work. Jim uses $\frac{2}{5}$ of a gallon.**

    Without using a calculator, work out who uses the most petrol.

    ....
    (2 marks)

7. **Evaluate $\dfrac{3^5}{3^3 \div 1^8}$ without using a calculator.**

    Give your answer as an ordinary number.

    ....
    (2 marks)

    Score: $\dfrac{}{10}$

Bonus Brainteaser

Zoe from Q6 pays £8 per gallon of petrol.
Without using a calculator, work out how much
it costs her to drive to and from work?

£ ....

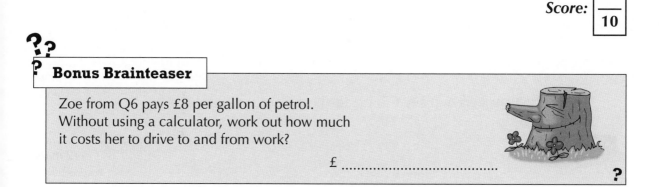

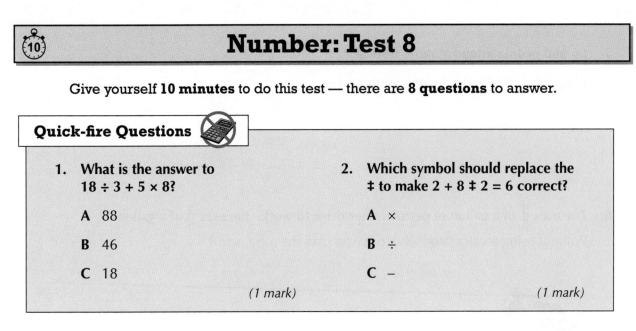

Number: Test 8

Give yourself **10 minutes** to do this test — there are **8 questions** to answer.

Quick-fire Questions

1. **What is the answer to**
    18 ÷ 3 + 5 × 8?

    A 88

    B 46

    C 18

    (1 mark)

2. **Which symbol should replace the**
    ‡ to make 2 + 8 ‡ 2 = 6 correct?

    A ×

    B ÷

    C −

    (1 mark)

3. **Write down the first five multiples of 8.**

    .... , ... , ... , ... , ...
    (1 mark)

4. **A caravan costs £22 per night. A hotel costs £134 per night.**

    Violet is going on holiday for 14 nights. Without using a calculator,
    work out how much she will save by staying in a caravan rather than in a hotel.

    £ ....
    (2 marks)

5. **Work out $\frac{4}{5} \times \frac{7}{8}$ without using a calculator.**

   Give your answer as a fraction in its simplest form.

   ....
   (1 mark)

6. **Evaluate $3.5^2 + 0.8^3$.**

   ....
   (1 mark)

7. **Show that 113 is a prime number.**

   ....

   ....

   ....
   (2 marks)

8. **Rupinder is knitting a scarf. At the start of the week, it was 60 cm long. By the end of the week, it was 72 cm long.**

   Find the length of the scarf at the end of the week as a percentage of its length at the start of the week.

   .... %
   (1 mark)

   Score: $\dfrac{}{10}$

Number: Test 9

Give yourself **10 minutes** to do this test — there are **7 questions** to answer.

Quick-fire Questions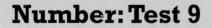

1. What is $\frac{4}{24}$ in its simplest form?

    A $\frac{2}{12}$ B $\frac{1}{6}$ C $\frac{1}{8}$

    (1 mark)

2. What is 5% of 120?

    A 24   B 1.2   C 6

    (1 mark)

3. Put these numbers in order of size, starting with the smallest.

−7	10	3	0	−14	−1

    .... , ... , ... , ... , ... , ...

    (1 mark)

4. **A shop sells buckets for 75p each and spades for 59p each.**

    Without using a calculator, calculate how much
    12 buckets and 10 spades would cost in total.

    £ ....

    (2 marks)

5. **What is the highest common factor of 28 and 35?**

    ....

    (1 mark)

6. **Evaluate the following:**

$\sqrt[3]{216}$

....
(1 mark)

$\sqrt[4]{81}$

....
(1 mark)

7. **The diagram shows a rectangular bed of soil.**

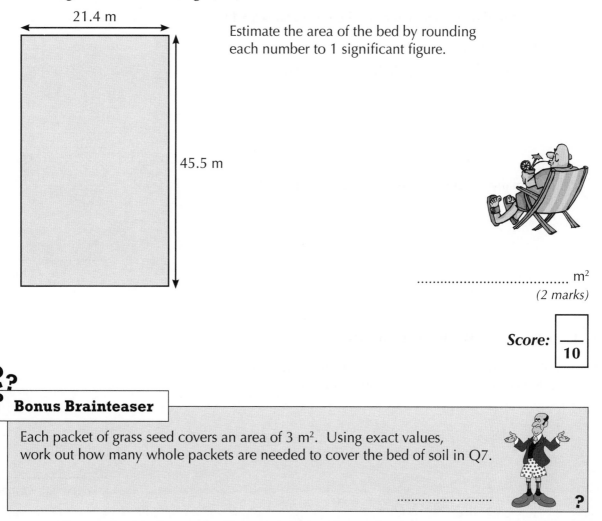

21.4 m

45.5 m

Estimate the area of the bed by rounding each number to 1 significant figure.

.... m²
(2 marks)

Score: $\dfrac{\quad}{10}$

?₂?
?

Bonus Brainteaser

Each packet of grass seed covers an area of 3 m². Using exact values, work out how many whole packets are needed to cover the bed of soil in Q7.

.... **?**

Give yourself **10 minutes** to do this test — there are **7 questions** to answer.

Quick-fire Questions

1. **What is 428 m in km?**

   A 0.428 km

   B 4.28 km

   C 42.8 km

   (1 mark)

2. **1 foot ≈ 30 cm. Approximately how many cm are there in 3 feet?**

   A 10 cm

   B 90 cm

   C 3 cm

   (1 mark)

3. **The ratio of seals to penguins at the local zoo is 2 : 11.**

   Without using a calculator, work out:

   how many seals there are if there are 88 penguins,

   ....
   (1 mark)

   how many penguins there are if there are 12 seals.

   ....
   (1 mark)

4. **3 teenagers take 30 selfies in 1 day.**

   Without using a calculator, work out how many selfies
   3 teenagers would take in 5 days at this rate.

   ....
   (1 mark)

5. A map of a town is shown below. The scale of the map is 1 cm = 3 km.

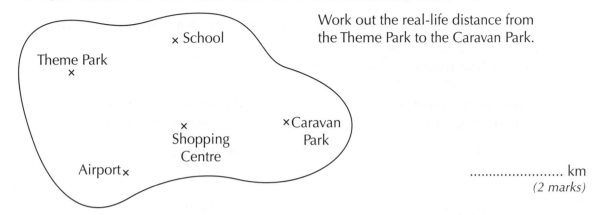

Work out the real-life distance from the Theme Park to the Caravan Park.

.... km
(2 marks)

6. An adult ticket to the theatre costs £40. A child's ticket is 20% less than an adult ticket.

Without using a calculator, work out the cost of a child's ticket to the theatre.

£ ....
(1 mark)

7. Andy started his bike race at 9:00 am. He crossed the finish line at 12:30 pm. His average speed during the race was 22 km/h.

How long was the race, in kilometres?

.... km
(2 marks)

Score: $\dfrac{}{10}$

Give yourself **10 minutes** to do this test — there are **6 questions** to answer.

Quick-fire Questions 🚫🖩

1. **How is 21:35 written using the 12-hour clock?**

   A 9:35 pm

   B 9:35 am

   C 11:35 pm

   (1 mark)

2. **What time is 3 hours and 20 minutes after 8:15 am?**

   A 11:35 pm

   B 10:35 am

   C 11:35 am

   (1 mark)

3. **8 jars of chutney cost £12.40.**

   How much do 5 jars of chutney cost?

   £ ....
   (2 marks)

4. **Rachel is comparing how far she has to run, swim and cycle in her upcoming race.**

	Run	Swim	Cycle
Distance	5 miles	7952 m	7.4 km

   Given that 5 miles ≈ 8 km, which part of the race is the shortest?

   ....
   (2 marks)

---

5. **Gabriel makes a scale drawing of his garden, using a scale of 1 : 80.**

He draws a pond 6 cm wide. How wide is the pond, in cm, in real life?

.... cm
(1 mark)

His garden shed is 2.4 m wide in real life.
How wide, in cm, would the shed be on Gabriel's drawing?

.... cm
(2 marks)

6. **Oscar the rabbit weighed 800 g in January. He weighed 20% more in November.**

How much, in grams, did he weigh in November?

.... g
(1 mark)

Score: | $\dfrac{}{10}$

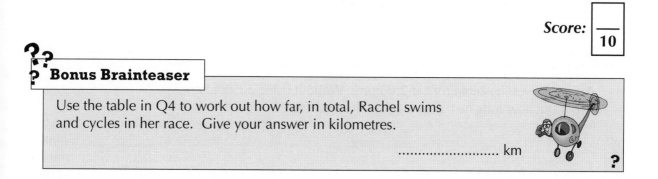

Bonus Brainteaser

Use the table in Q4 to work out how far, in total, Rachel swims
and cycles in her race. Give your answer in kilometres.

.... km

?

Give yourself **10 minutes** to do this test — there are **6 questions** to answer.

Quick-fire Questions 🚫🖩

1. **What is 8 : 32 in its simplest form?**

   A 1 : 4

   B 2 : 8

   C 4 : 1

   (1 mark)

2. **What is 35 kg : 7 kg simplified?**

   A 1 : 5

   B 5 : 7

   C 5 : 1

   (1 mark)

3. **Oli sells 18 litres of homemade lemonade at a music festival.**

   Given that 1 gallon ≈ 4.5 litres, approximately how many gallons of lemonade does Oli sell?

   .... gallons
   (1 mark)

4. **A ferry timetable is given below.**

Windowmere	12:22	14:15	16:24	18:37
Amblefront	12:45	14:30	16:52	18:54
Lake Edge	13:30	15:21	17:44	19:34
Brocktunnel	13:43	15:31	18:01	19:48

   When does the last ferry from Windowmere arrive at Brocktunnel?
   Give your answer using the 12-hour clock.

   ....
   (1 mark)

   James arrives in Amblefront at 2:05 pm. Without using a calculator,
   work out how long he has to wait for the next ferry.

   .... minutes
   (1 mark)

5. **"A Taste of Italy" sells three different sized bags of fresh pasta.**

Small	**Medium**	**Large**
1.5 kg	2 kg	5 kg
£1.98	£3.29	£6.32

Which size bag of pasta represents the best value for money?

....

(3 marks)

6. **Constance decides to invest her money in a savings scheme that pays 2% simple interest each year.**

She opens the savings scheme by investing £260 and leaves it untouched for 3 years. How much money will she have in total at the end of the 3 years?

£ ....

(2 marks)

Score: | $\frac{}{10}$ |

Give yourself **10 minutes** to do this test — there are **6 questions** to answer.

1. **Eva walks 24 km in 4 hours. What is her average speed?**

   A 8 km/h

   B 6 km/h

   C 96 km/h

   (1 mark)

2. **Otto runs 200 m in 50 seconds. What is his average speed?**

   A 40 m/s

   B 10 m/s

   C 4 m/s

   (1 mark)

3. **Lucy goes to see her favourite band, '10 Minutes of Winter'. The concert starts at 7:40 pm and lasts 2 hours and 40 minutes.**

   What time does the concert finish? Give your answer in the 24-hour clock.

   ....
   (2 marks)

4. **3 painters can paint 9 fences in one day.**

   Assuming they work at the same rate, how many fences could 5 painters paint in one day? Do not use a calculator.

   ....
   (1 mark)

5. **Zarek made a scale drawing of his kitchen using the scale 1 : 50.**

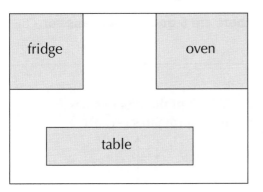

Without using a calculator, work out the
real-life length of the longest side of his table.
Give your answer in metres.

.... m

(2 marks)

6. **Stan and Laurel have their own car washing business. On Saturday, Stan spent
three hours cleaning cars. Laurel spent two more hours cleaning cars than Stan.**

Stan and Laurel made £56 in total on Saturday and decided to
share the money in the ratio of how many hours they spent cleaning.
How much money did Laurel get?

£ ....

(3 marks)

Score: $\frac{}{10}$

?? Bonus Brainteaser

What fraction of the total money Stan and Laurel earned in Q6
did Laurel get? Give your answer in its simplest form.

....

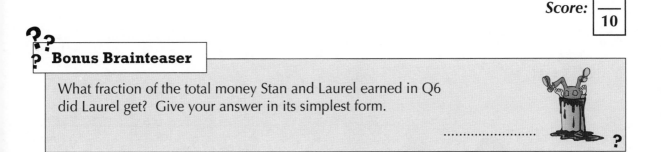

Algebra: Test 1

Give yourself **10 minutes** to do this test — there are **6 questions** to answer.

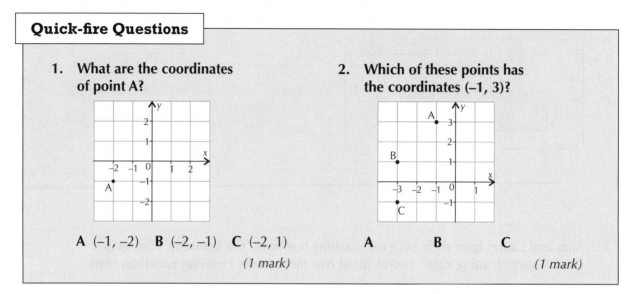

Quick-fire Questions

1. **What are the coordinates of point A?**

    A (–1, –2)   **B** (–2, –1)   **C** (–2, 1)

    (1 mark)

2. **Which of these points has the coordinates (–1, 3)?**

    A   B   C

    (1 mark)

3. **Look at the formula below.**

    $$E = 12(20 - F)$$

    Without using a calculator, find *E* when *F* = 8.

    E = ...
    (2 marks)

4. **Solve the equations below to find the value of the missing letters.**

    $3s = 18$

    s = ...
    (1 mark)

    $u - 5 = 31$

    u = ...
    (1 mark)

5. Use the grid below to answer this question.

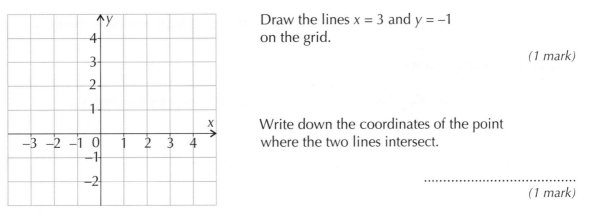

Draw the lines $x = 3$ and $y = -1$
on the grid.

(1 mark)

Write down the coordinates of the point
where the two lines intersect.

....

(1 mark)

6. The graph below shows Rimi's bike ride.

She sets off from home at 13:00 and cycles to the park, where she stops for lunch.
She then cycles on to the beach, where she stops again, before cycling all the way home.

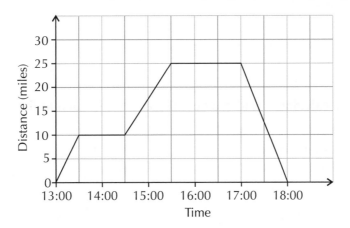

How long does she cycle for in total?

.... hours and .... minutes

(2 marks)

Score: $\dfrac{}{10}$

Give yourself **10 minutes** to do this test — there are **6 questions** to answer.

1. $x \times y \times 4y$ simplified is...

    A $4xy$

    B $x + 4y^2$

    C $4xy^2$

    (1 mark)

2. $10a - y - a$ simplified is...

    A $10 - y$

    B $9a - y$

    C $a - y$

    (1 mark)

3. **To find Jake's test score, multiply Alan's test score by 3, then subtract 7.**

    If Alan's test score is 25, what is Jake's test score?

    ....
    (1 mark)

4. **Without using your calculator, find the next three terms in each of the sequences below.**

    Multiply the previous term by 4:   1, ... , ... , ...
    (1 mark)

    Subtract 6 from the previous term: 50, ... , ... , ...
    (1 mark)

5. **Fiona is thinking of a number.**
    She says, "If you multiply my number by 5, then add 6, you get y."

    Fiona's original number was x. Write down a formula for y in terms of x.

    ....
    (2 marks)

6. **The equation of a straight line is $y - 2x = 1$.**

    Which of the options below shows another way of writing this equation?

    | A $y = 1 - 2x$ | B $y = 2x + 1$ | C $y = -1 - 2x$ | D $y = 2x - 1$ |

    ....
    (1 mark)

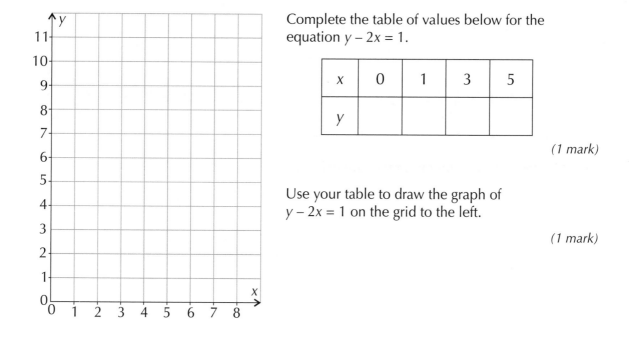

Complete the table of values below for the equation $y - 2x = 1$.

x	0	1	3	5
y				

(1 mark)

Use your table to draw the graph of $y - 2x = 1$ on the grid to the left.

(1 mark)

Score: $\dfrac{}{10}$

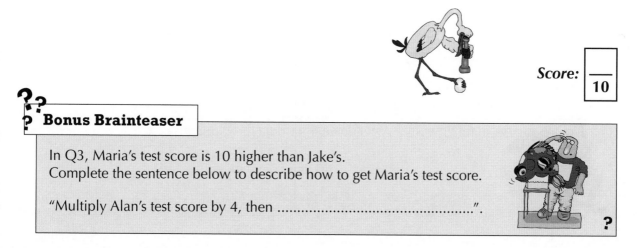

? Bonus Brainteaser

In Q3, Maria's test score is 10 higher than Jake's.
Complete the sentence below to describe how to get Maria's test score.

"Multiply Alan's test score by 4, then ....".

Algebra: Test 2

Algebra: Test 3

Give yourself **10 minutes** to do this test — there are **7 questions** to answer.

Quick-fire Questions

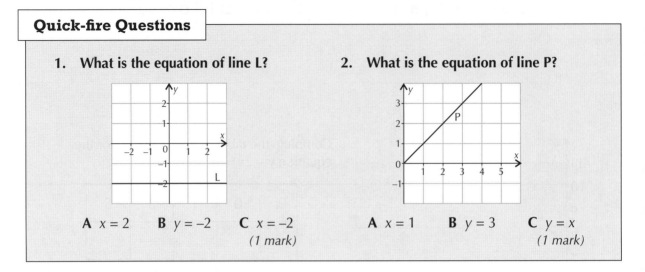

1. What is the equation of line L?

   A $x = 2$ **B** $y = -2$ **C** $x = -2$
   (1 mark)

2. What is the equation of line P?

   A $x = 1$ **B** $y = 3$ **C** $y = x$
   (1 mark)

3. Plot the following points on the grid below.

   W $(-3, 5)$ **X** $(0, 4)$ **Y** $(1, -4)$ **Z** $(-2, 0)$

(2 marks)

4. Jaspreet has a basket of *C* carrots. She gives half of them to Ben.
   She then gives 4 carrots to Kim. Jaspreet now has *D* carrots left.

   Which of the formulas below gives the value of *D*? Circle the correct answer.

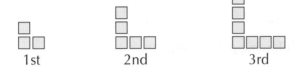

$$D = \frac{C}{4} - 2 \qquad D = C - 2 - 4 \qquad D = 2C - 4 \qquad D = \frac{C}{2} - 4$$

(1 mark)

5. Below are the first three patterns of a sequence.

   1st   2nd   3rd

   How many squares will there be in the 4th and 5th patterns?

   4th: .... 5th: ....
   (2 marks)

6. Solve the equation below to find *t*.

   $t - 9 = 2 - 10t$

   $t = $ ....
   (2 marks)

7. Use the equation $5x + 6 = 32$ to find the value of $5x - 6$.

   $5x - 6 = $ ....
   (1 mark)

Score: $\dfrac{\quad}{10}$

Algebra: Test 4

Give yourself **10 minutes** to do this test — there are **6 questions** to answer.

Quick-fire Questions

1. Multiplying out the brackets in $4(k + 9)$ gives...

   A $4k + 9$

   B $4k + 36$

   C $4k + 13$

   (1 mark)

2. Solving the equation $z - 5 = 18$ for z gives...

   A $z = 13$

   B $z = 23$

   C $z = 90$

   (1 mark)

---

3. Jill writes down the following expression.

$$8x - 12$$

Find the value of the expression when:

$x = 1$

....
(1 mark)

$x = 10$

....
(1 mark)

4. **A sports shop prints names and numbers on the back of football shirts. It costs £5 for the full number, plus £1 for every letter in the name.**

Write down a formula for the total cost (£C) of printing a number and a name with n letters.

....
(1 mark)

---

5. The conversion graph below shows the cost of sweets per gram.

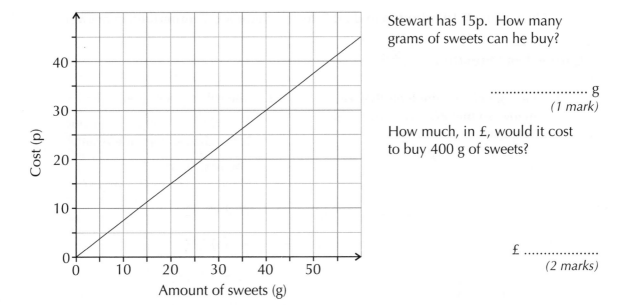

Stewart has 15p. How many grams of sweets can he buy?

.... g
(1 mark)

How much, in £, would it cost to buy 400 g of sweets?

£ ....
(2 marks)

6. Look at the sequence shown below.

$$-9, -5, -1, 3, ...$$

Find the *n*th term of the sequence.

*n*th term = ...
(2 marks)

Score: $\dfrac{}{10}$

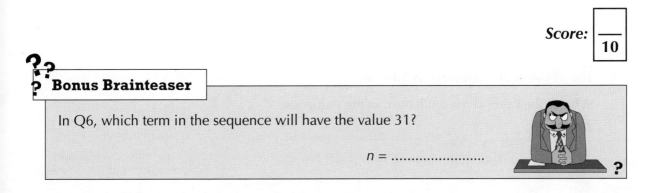

Bonus Brainteaser

In Q6, which term in the sequence will have the value 31?

n = ...

Give yourself **10 minutes** to do this test — there are **7 questions** to answer.

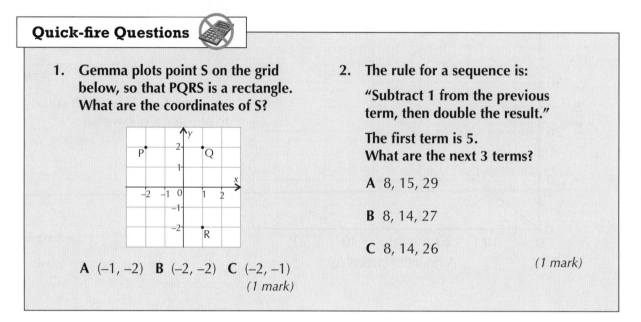

Quick-fire Questions

1. Gemma plots point S on the grid below, so that PQRS is a rectangle. What are the coordinates of S?

    A (–1, –2)   **B** (–2, –2)   **C** (–2, –1)

    (1 mark)

2. The rule for a sequence is:

    "Subtract 1 from the previous term, then double the result."

    The first term is 5.
    What are the next 3 terms?

    A 8, 15, 29

    B 8, 14, 27

    C 8, 14, 26

    (1 mark)

3. A famous formula in physics is *E = mgh*.

    Find the value of *E* when *m* = 2.5, *g* = 10 and *h* = 4.

    E = ...
    (1 mark)

4. Solve the equation below to find the value of *p*.

    p + 10 = –2

    p = ...
    (1 mark)

5. The *n*th term of a sequence is 50 – 3*n*.

    What is the value of the tenth term in the sequence?

    ....
    (1 mark)

6. **Expand the expression shown below. Simplify your answer.**

$2(2a + 1) + a(4 + a) + 3(3 + 3a)$

....
(2 marks)

7. **The equation of a straight line is $y = 2x - 5$.**

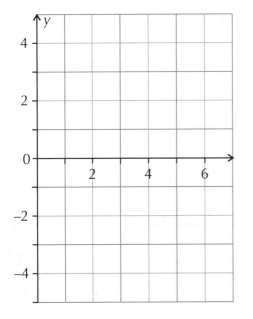

Complete the table of values below for the equation $y = 2x - 5$.

x	0	1	2	3
y				

(1 mark)

Use your table to draw the graph of $y = 2x - 5$ on the grid to the left.

(1 mark)

Write down the coordinates of the point where the line $y = 2x - 5$ crosses the x-axis.

....
(1 mark)

Score: $\dfrac{}{10}$

Give yourself **10 minutes** to do this test — there are **7 questions** to answer.

Quick-fire Questions

1. How many lines of symmetry does the capital letter E have?

   A 1

   B 2

   C 3

   (1 mark)

2. Which symbol has rotational symmetry of order 2?

   A >

   B £

   C %

   (1 mark)

3. Find the volume of the cuboid below.

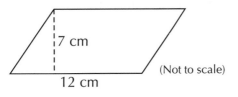

(Not to scale)

3.1 cm   8 cm

6.2 cm

.... cm³
(1 mark)

4. Without using a calculator, find the area of the parallelogram below.

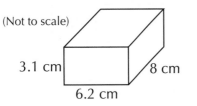

7 cm

12 cm   (Not to scale)

.... cm²
(1 mark)

5. Find the size of angle x in the isosceles triangle below.

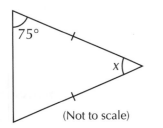

75°

x

(Not to scale)

$x =$ .... °
(2 marks)

6. **A circular rug has a diameter of 1.5 m.**

   What is the area of the rug? Give your answer to 2 decimal places.

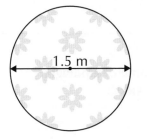

1.5 m

.... m²
(2 marks)

7. **Accurately complete the net of this triangular prism in the space below. Label the sides.**

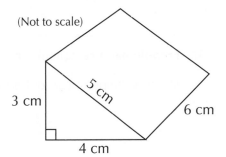

(Not to scale)

3 cm

5 cm

4 cm

6 cm

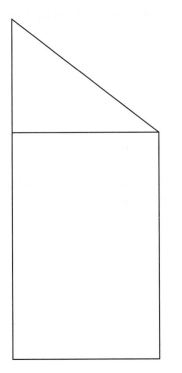

(2 marks)

Score:

Give yourself **10 minutes** to do this test — there are **6 questions** to answer.

1. **Which of these shapes is a regular quadrilateral?**

    A rectangle

    B rhombus

    C square

    (1 mark)

2. **What is the name of a polygon that has eight sides?**

    A heptagon

    B octagon

    C hexagon

    (1 mark)

3. **Freddie has a rectangular poster that measures 30 cm by 45 cm.**

    What is the perimeter of his poster?

    .... cm
    (1 mark)

    45 cm

    30 cm   (Not to scale)

    Freddie buys another poster the same size and sticks the two posters together (see below). What is the perimeter of his new giant poster?

    (Not to scale)

    .... cm
    (2 marks)

4. **Find the size of angle p in the diagram below.**

    34°

    p

    (Not to scale)

    $p = $ .... °
    (1 mark)

5. **Triangle XYZ has sides XY = 6 cm, XZ = 4 cm and ZY = 5 cm.**

Construct triangle XYZ in the space below. Side XY has been drawn for you.

X   Y

(2 marks)

6. **The net of a cuboid is shown below.**

Use the net to work out the surface area of the cuboid.

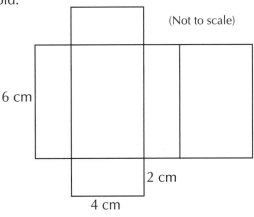

(Not to scale)

6 cm

2 cm

4 cm

.... cm²
(2 marks)

Score: $\dfrac{\quad}{10}$

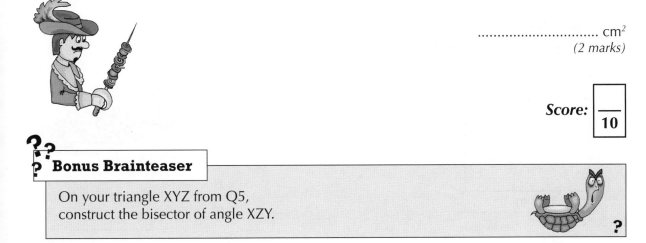

Bonus Brainteaser

On your triangle XYZ from Q5,
construct the bisector of angle XZY.

Give yourself **10 minutes** to do this test — there are **7 questions** to answer.

Quick-fire Questions

1. **How many vertices does a triangular prism have?**

   A 4

   B 5

   C 6

   (1 mark)

2. **What is the name of this 3D shape?**

   A square-based pyramid

   B triangular prism

   C regular tetrahedron

   (1 mark)

3. **Draw all the lines of symmetry on the shape below.**

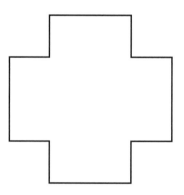

(1 mark)

4. **Gustav has a rectangular garden with an area of 28 m².
   The length of his garden is 8 m.**

   What is the width of his garden?

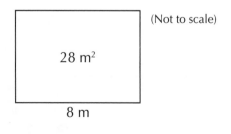

(Not to scale)

28 m²

8 m

.... m

(1 mark)

5. Shape P has been rotated clockwise to give shape Q.

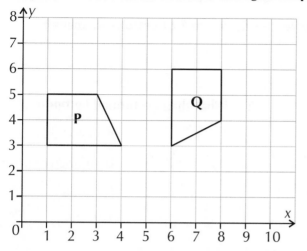

Mark a cross (×) on the diagram to show the centre of rotation.

(1 mark)

What is the angle of rotation?

.... °

(1 mark)

6. The prism on the right has a cross-sectional area of 12 cm².

What is its volume?

(Not to scale)

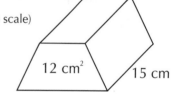

12 cm²   15 cm

.... cm³

(1 mark)

7. Find the size of angle *w* in the irregular pentagon below.

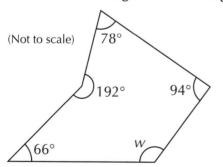

(Not to scale)   78°

192°   94°

66°   *w*

w = ... °

(3 marks)

Score: —
10

Geometry and Measures: Test 3

Geometry and Measures: Test 4

Give yourself **10 minutes** to do this test — there are **7 questions** to answer.

Quick-fire Questions

1. Which of these nets will **not** fold to make a cube?

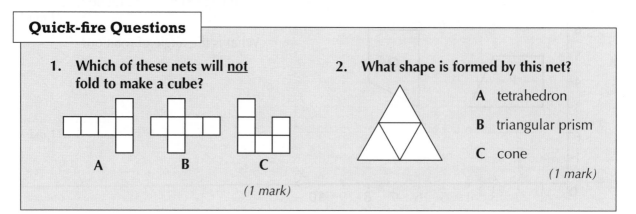

   A   B   C

   (1 mark)

2. What shape is formed by this net?

   A tetrahedron

   B triangular prism

   C cone

   (1 mark)

3. Reflect shape A in the mirror line.

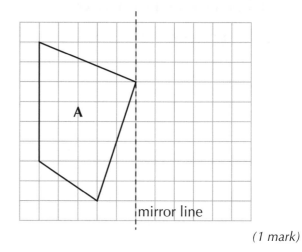

   mirror line

   (1 mark)

4. The isosceles triangle below has a perimeter of 24 cm.

   Find the lengths of the two missing sides.

   9 cm

   (Not to scale)

   .... cm and .... cm

   (1 mark)

5. Shape M is shown on the coordinate grid below.

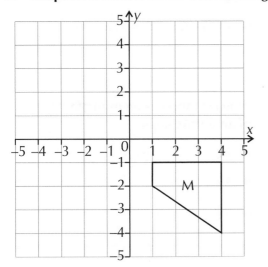

Translate shape M by the vector $\begin{pmatrix} -5 \\ 4 \end{pmatrix}$.

Label the image N.

(2 marks)

6. Find the sizes of angles *a* and *b* in the diagram below.

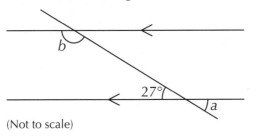

(Not to scale)

$a = $ ....$^{\circ}$

$b = $ ....$^{\circ}$

(2 marks)

7. Use a ruler and a pair of compasses to construct the perpendicular bisector of line AB.

A •

B •

(2 marks)

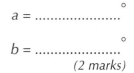

Score: | 10

Geometry and Measures: Test 5

Give yourself **10 minutes** to do this test — there are **6 questions** to answer.

Quick-fire Questions

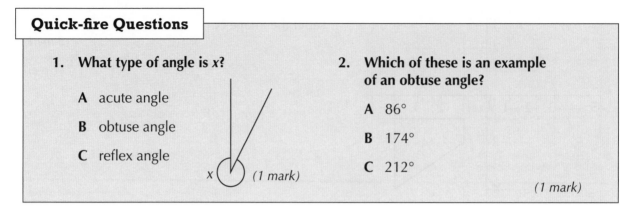

1. **What type of angle is *x*?**

    A acute angle

    B obtuse angle

    C reflex angle

    x *(1 mark)*

2. **Which of these is an example of an obtuse angle?**

    A 86°

    B 174°

    C 212°

    (1 mark)

3. **Here is a hexagonal prism.**

    How many vertices does the prism have?

    ....
    (1 mark)

    How many faces does the prism have?

    ....
    (1 mark)

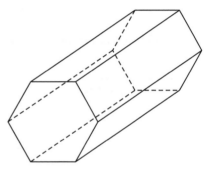

4. **Here are seven quadrilaterals labelled A-G.**

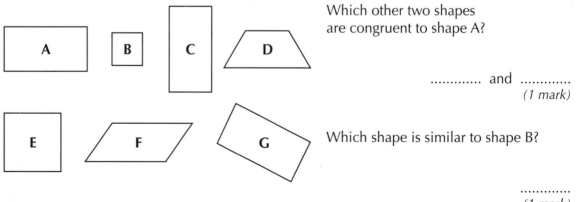

    Which other two shapes are congruent to shape A?

    .... and ....
    (1 mark)

    Which shape is similar to shape B?

    ....
    (1 mark)

5. **Serena's tent is a triangular prism, as shown below.**

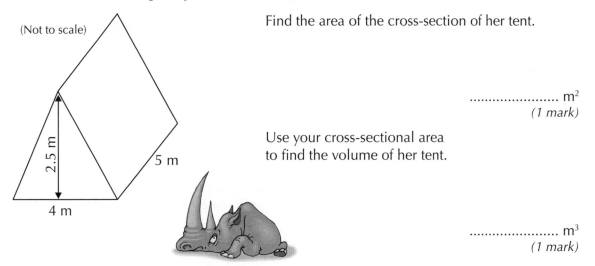

(Not to scale)

2.5 m

4 m

5 m

Find the area of the cross-section of her tent.

.... m²
(1 mark)

Use your cross-sectional area
to find the volume of her tent.

.... m³
(1 mark)

6. **On the grid below, shape K is an enlargement of shape J.**

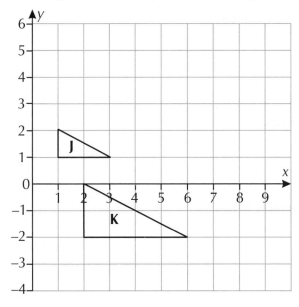

What is the scale factor
of the enlargement?

....
(1 mark)

What is the centre of enlargement?

....
(1 mark)

Score:

—
10

?
??
Bonus Brainteaser

On the axes above, enlarge triangle J by a scale factor of 3
and centre of enlargement (0, 0). What are the coordinates
of the vertices of the enlarged shape?

.... , ... and ....

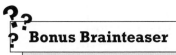

?

(10)

Give yourself **10 minutes** to do this test — there are **6 questions** to answer.

Quick-fire Questions

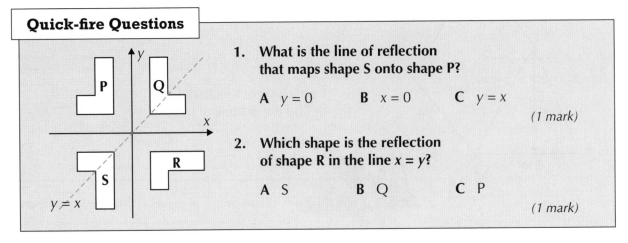

1. **What is the line of reflection that maps shape S onto shape P?**

   A $y = 0$ **B** $x = 0$ **C** $y = x$

   (1 mark)

2. **Which shape is the reflection of shape R in the line $x = y$?**

   A S   **B** Q   **C** P

   (1 mark)

3. **The shape below is a regular decagon.**

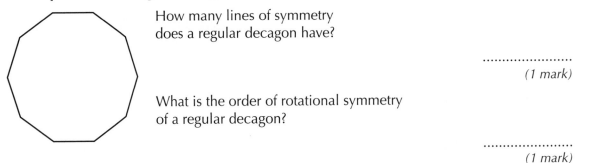

   How many lines of symmetry
   does a regular decagon have?

   ....
   (1 mark)

   What is the order of rotational symmetry
   of a regular decagon?

   ....
   (1 mark)

4. **Find the missing angles in each of the diagrams below.**

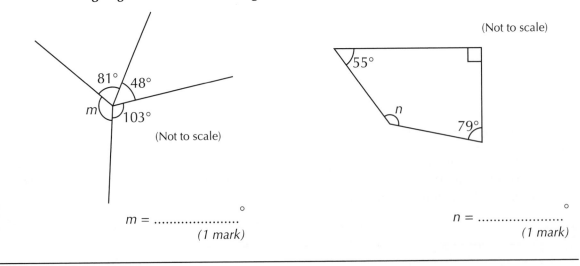

(Not to scale)

   $m =$ ....$^{\circ}$
   (1 mark)

   $n =$ ....$^{\circ}$
   (1 mark)

5. Find the area of the shape below.

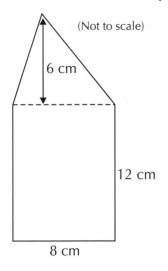

(Not to scale)

6 cm

12 cm

8 cm

.... cm²
(2 marks)

6. Imran has a plastic counter in the shape of a circle with a square cut out of it.
The circle has a radius of **7 cm** and the square has sides of length **5 cm**.

What is the area of the plastic?
Give your answer to 2 decimal places.

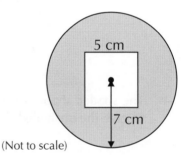

5 cm

7 cm

(Not to scale)

.... cm²
(2 marks)

Score:

Give yourself **10 minutes** to do this test — there are **7 questions** to answer.

Quick-fire Questions

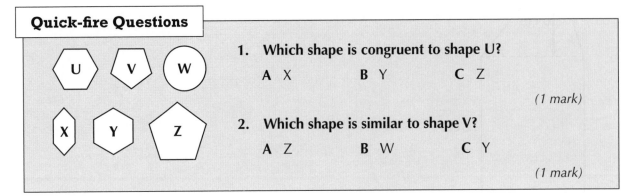

1. **Which shape is congruent to shape U?**

    A X   B Y   C Z

    (1 mark)

2. **Which shape is similar to shape V?**

    A Z   B W   C Y

    (1 mark)

3. **Using the line given below as the base line, draw an angle of 25°.**

    _____

    (1 mark)

4. **The shaded shape is rotated 90° clockwise about the point marked O to give the unshaded shape, as shown below.**

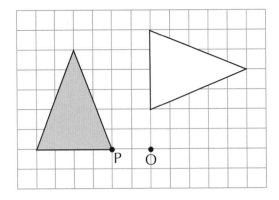

On the unshaded shape, draw a cross (×) to show the new position of point P.

(1 mark)

5. Find the size of angles *u*, *v* and *w* in the diagram below.

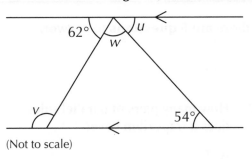

62°

w

u

v

54°

(Not to scale)

$u = $ .... °

$v = $ .... °

$w = $ .... °

(3 marks)

6. Enlarge shape F by a scale factor of 3.

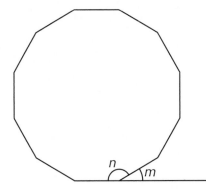

F

(1 mark)

7. The diagram below shows a regular dodecagon (a 12-sided shape).

Find the size of the exterior angle *m*.

n

m

$m = $ .... °

(1 mark)

Find the size of the interior angle *n*.

$n = $ .... °

(1 mark)

Score: $\dfrac{}{10}$

Geometry and Measures: Test 7

Give yourself **10 minutes** to do this test — there are **6 questions** to answer.

Quick-fire Questions

1. **What type of triangle has sides measuring 6 cm, 4 cm and 6 cm?**

    A scalene

    B equilateral

    C isosceles

    (1 mark)

2. **How many pairs of parallel sides does a trapezium have?**

    A 0

    B 1

    C 2

    (1 mark)

3. **Draw an accurate net of this cuboid in the space below. Label the sides.**

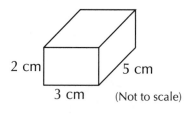

2 cm   3 cm   5 cm   (Not to scale)

(2 marks)

4. Find the size of angles *a* and *b* in the diagram below.

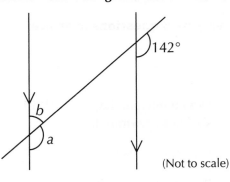

142°

b

a

(Not to scale)

$a = $ ....°

$b = $ ....°

(2 marks)

5. Farmer Reynolds wants to mark out a circular enclosure for his goats.
He pushes a stake into the ground and uses a tight piece of string to draw a circle.

The string is 1.4 m long.
What will the circumference of the enclosure be?
Give your answer to 2 decimal places.

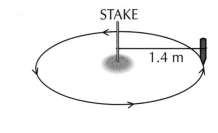

STAKE

1.4 m

.... m
(2 marks)

6. Bisect angle ABC.

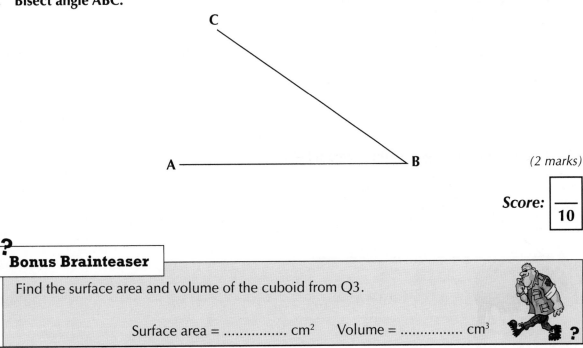

C

A

B

(2 marks)

Score: $\dfrac{}{10}$

??
? **Bonus Brainteaser**

Find the surface area and volume of the cuboid from Q3.

Surface area = ... cm²   Volume = ... cm³

?

Geometry and Measures: Test 9

Give yourself **10 minutes** to do this test — there are **6 questions** to answer.

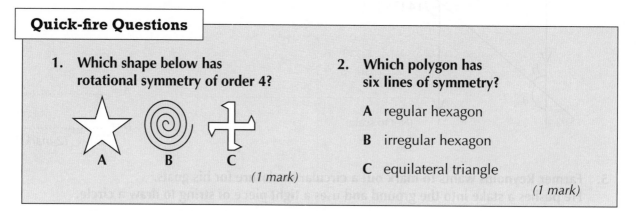

Quick-fire Questions

1. Which shape below has rotational symmetry of order 4?

   A   B   C

   (1 mark)

2. Which polygon has six lines of symmetry?

   A   regular hexagon

   B   irregular hexagon

   C   equilateral triangle

   (1 mark)

3. For the diagram below, find the translation vector that maps:

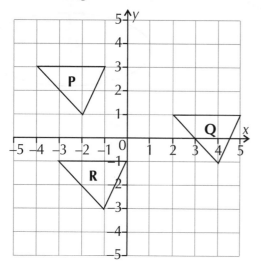

   Shape P onto shape Q.

   ....
   (1 mark)

   Shape Q onto shape R.

   ....
   (1 mark)

4. Find the missing angles in the diagram below.

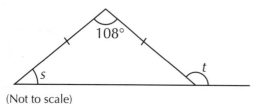

   108°

   s

   t

   (Not to scale)

   s = ... °

   t = ... °

   (2 marks)

5. **Rotate shape T 90° anticlockwise about the origin.**

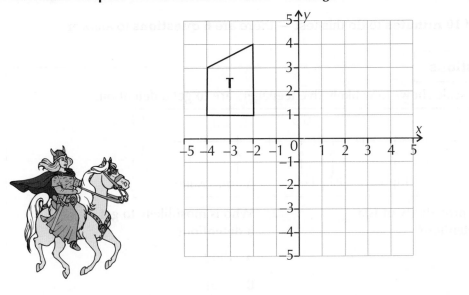

(2 marks)

6. **The cylinder below has a radius of 4.2 cm and a height of 12.8 cm.**

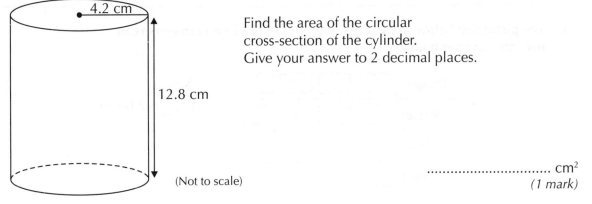

(Not to scale)

Find the area of the circular
cross-section of the cylinder.
Give your answer to 2 decimal places.

.... cm²
(1 mark)

Use the cross-sectional area to find the volume of the cylinder.
Give your answer to 2 decimal places.

.... cm³
(1 mark)

Score: $\dfrac{}{10}$

Give yourself **10 minutes** to do this test — there are **6 questions** to answer.

Quick-fire Questions

This probability scale shows how likely five teenagers are to get a detention.

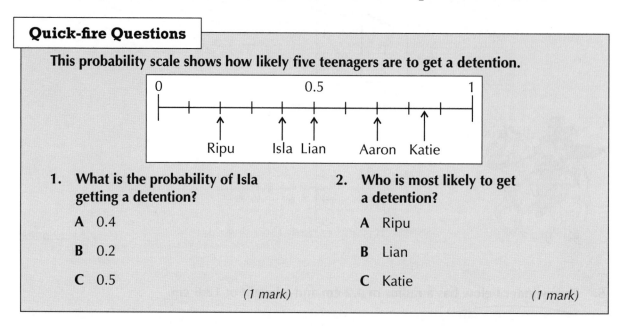

1. **What is the probability of Isla getting a detention?**

   A   0.4

   B   0.2

   C   0.5

   (1 mark)

2. **Who is most likely to get a detention?**

   A   Ripu

   B   Lian

   C   Katie

   (1 mark)

3. **The pictogram below shows the number of books four teenagers read over the summer holidays.**

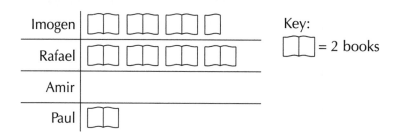

How many books did Rafael read?

....

(1 mark)

Amir read 5 books. Complete the pictogram to show this information.

(1 mark)

How many books were read in total?

....

(1 mark)

4. **Lola records the ages of the children she babysits for.**

$$7, \quad 6, \quad 4, \quad 8, \quad 3, \quad 7, \quad 6, \quad 7$$

What is the range of the ages?

....
(1 mark)

What is the mode?

....
(1 mark)

5. **Michael weighs some watermelons and records their weights.**

Are the weights of the watermelons discrete or continuous data?

....
(1 mark)

6. **A shop owner records the outside temperature and the number of scarves she sells each day. Her results are shown on the scatter graph below.**

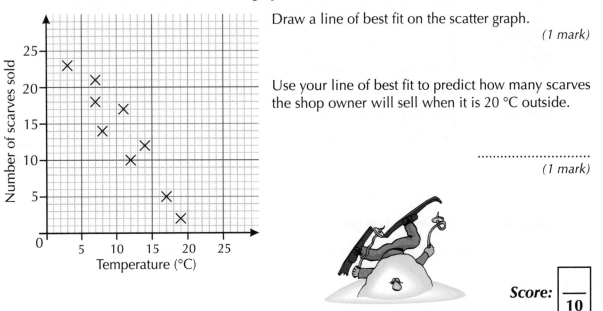

Draw a line of best fit on the scatter graph.

(1 mark)

Use your line of best fit to predict how many scarves the shop owner will sell when it is 20 °C outside.

....
(1 mark)

Score:

$$\frac{}{10}$$

Probability and Statistics: Test 2

Give yourself **10 minutes** to do this test — there are **7 questions** to answer.

Quick-fire Questions

The number of bedrooms in people's houses is shown in the graph below.

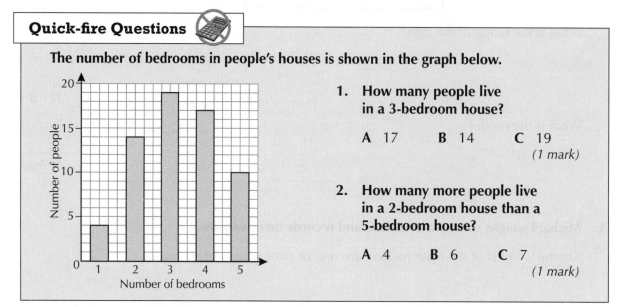

1. **How many people live in a 3-bedroom house?**

   A   17   B   14   C   19

   (1 mark)

2. **How many more people live in a 2-bedroom house than a 5-bedroom house?**

   A   4   B   6   C   7

   (1 mark)

3. An auction house records the number of antiques sold each month for 6 months. The results are shown in the table below.

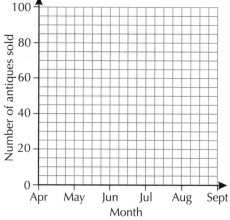

Month	Number of antiques sold
Apr	25
May	40
Jun	70
Jul	55
Aug	30
Sept	65

Draw a line graph on the grid to show this data.

(1 mark)

4. The probability of Ryan visiting his grandma at the weekend is $\frac{5}{6}$.

   What is the probability that he doesn't visit his grandma at the weekend?

   ....

   (1 mark)

5. **Nancy records the highest temperature (in °C) each day for 5 days.**

18, 21, 22, 17, 19

    What was the mean temperature for these 5 days?

    .... °C
    (1 mark)

6. **Marcus tosses a fair coin and spins a fair 4-sided spinner.**
    The sample space diagram below shows all his possible outcomes.

	Red (R)	Blue (B)	Green (G)	Yellow (Y)
Heads (H)	HR			
Tails (T)				TY

    Complete the sample space diagram.
    (1 mark)

    What is the probability of getting a head and landing on blue?
    Give your answer as a fraction in its simplest form.

    ....
    (1 mark)

    What is the probability of getting a tail and landing on red or yellow?
    Give your answer as a fraction in its simplest form.

    ....
    (1 mark)

7. **The table shows the types of pets owned by Class 9B.**

    Work out the angles needed to draw a pie chart of the results.

Pet	Dog	Cat	Rabbit	Other
Frequency	15	8	5	2
Angle				

    (2 marks)

    Score: —/10

Probability and Statistics: Test 3

Give yourself **10 minutes** to do this test — there are **6 questions** to answer.

Quick-fire Questions

The scatter graphs show different variables for a group of people plotted against their age.

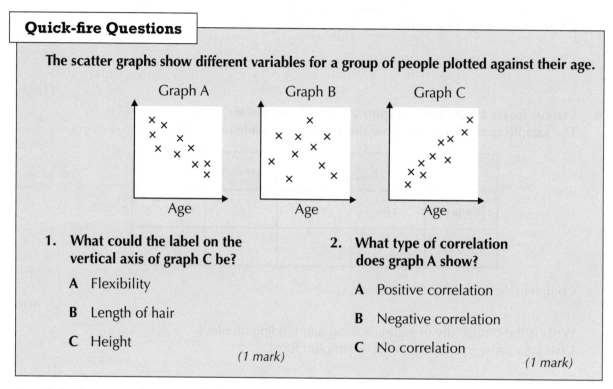

Graph A   Graph B   Graph C

Age   Age   Age

1. **What could the label on the vertical axis of graph C be?**

    A Flexibility

    B Length of hair

    C Height

    (1 mark)

2. **What type of correlation does graph A show?**

    A Positive correlation

    B Negative correlation

    C No correlation

    (1 mark)

3. **Eloise has some letter cards that spell out her name. She picks one card at random.**

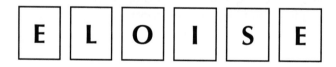

E L O I S E

What is the probability that she picks an E?
Give your answer as a fraction in its simplest form.

....
(1 mark)

What is the probability that she picks a vowel?
Give your answer as a fraction in its simplest form.

....
(1 mark)

4. **The dual bar chart shows the number of siblings a group of Year 7 students have.**

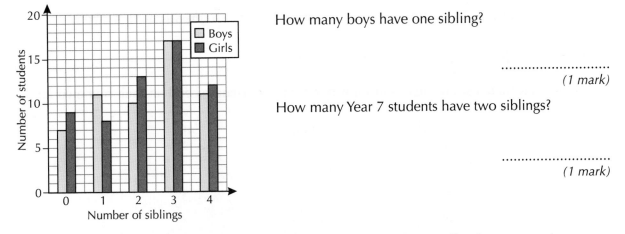

How many boys have one sibling?

....
(1 mark)

How many Year 7 students have two siblings?

....
(1 mark)

5. **Alix records the lengths (in minutes) of seven films in her DVD collection.**

94, 122, 108, 115, 99, 101, 125

What is the median film length?

.... minutes
(2 marks)

6. **A group of teenagers were asked what pets they had.**

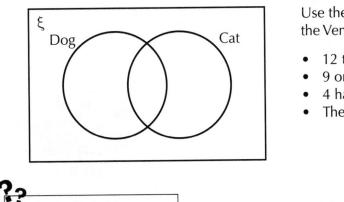

Use the information below to complete the Venn diagram on the left.

- 12 teenagers only had a dog,
- 9 only had a cat,
- 4 had both a cat and a dog,
- There were 35 teenagers in total.

(2 marks)

Score: $\frac{}{10}$

Bonus Brainteaser

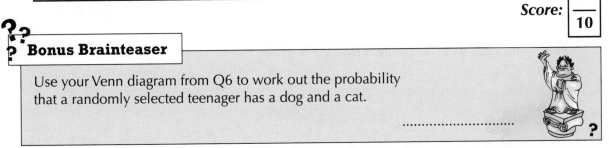

Use your Venn diagram from Q6 to work out the probability that a randomly selected teenager has a dog and a cat.

....

Give yourself **10 minutes** to do this test — there are **6 questions** to answer.

Quick-fire Questions

These pie charts show the proportions of time three friends spend on their homework.

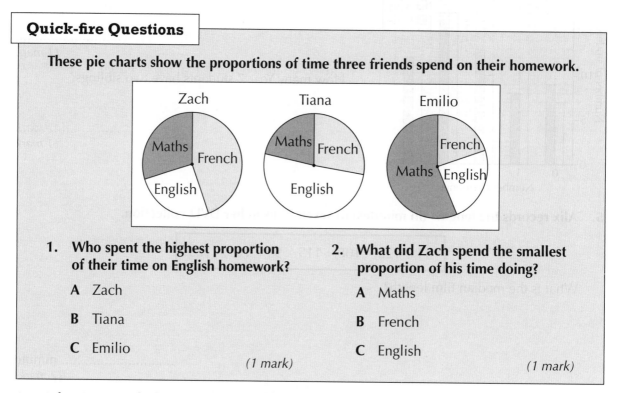

1. **Who spent the highest proportion of their time on English homework?**

   A Zach

   B Tiana

   C Emilio

   (1 mark)

2. **What did Zach spend the smallest proportion of his time doing?**

   A Maths

   B French

   C English

   (1 mark)

3. **A farmer records the number of eggs his hens lay each day for 5 days. He displays his results in the pictogram below.**

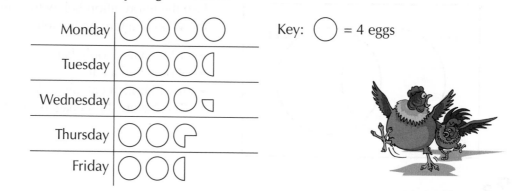

How many eggs were laid in total over the 5 days?

....

(1 mark)

4. The Venn diagram below shows the sets ξ, F and G .

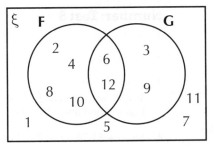

Write down the elements of set G.

....
(1 mark)

Write down the elements that are in **either** set F or set G.

....
(1 mark)

Work out n(F).

....
(1 mark)

5. The mean age of three brothers is 11. The oldest brother is 15 and the youngest brother is 8.

How old is the middle brother?

....
(1 mark)

6. The frequency table below shows the number of cars different families have.

Number of cars	0	1	2	3	4	Total
Frequency	5	12	14	6	3	
Number of cars × frequency	0	12				

Complete the table.

(2 marks)

Find the mean number of cars per family.

....
(1 mark)

Score: | —
10

Answers

Number: Test 1

1. A *(1 mark)*

2. B *(1 mark)*

3.
$$
\begin{array}{r}
1\ 3\ 7 \\
+\ \ \ 8\ 9 \\
\hline
2\ 2\ 6 \\
{\scriptstyle 1\ 1}
\end{array}
$$
(1 mark)

4. Multiples of 3: 6, 12, 21, 36 *(1 mark)*
   Factors of 24: 6, 8, 12 *(1 mark)*

5.
$$
\begin{array}{r}
3\ 4 \\
8\,\overline{)\,2\ 7^{3}2}
\end{array}
$$
(1 mark)

6. 9% = 0.09 *(1 mark)*
   100% − 27% = 73% = $\frac{73}{100}$ *(1 mark)*

7. 7836 = 7800 (2 s.f.) *(1 mark)*

8. $6^8 \times 6^2 = 6^{8+2} = 6^{10}$ *(1 mark)*

Number: Test 2

1. A *(1 mark)*

2. A *(1 mark)*

3. Carrot, beetroot, squash, parsnip *(1 mark)*

4. £65 and £6500 *(1 mark)*

5. 270 ÷ 3 = 90
   90 ÷ 10 = 9 days *(1 mark)*

6. $\frac{3}{4} + \frac{1}{6} = \frac{9}{12} + \frac{2}{12}$ *(1 mark)*

   $= \frac{11}{12}$ *(1 mark)*

7. Actual value = 7.69
   Rounded value = 7.7
   Error = 7.7 − 7.69 = 0.01 *(1 mark)*

8. $\sqrt{169} + \sqrt{225} = 13 + 15$ *(1 mark)*
   = 28 *(1 mark)*

BONUS BRAINTEASER

$\frac{2}{5}$ of 270 = (270 ÷ 5) × 2 = 108

Number: Test 3

1. B *(1 mark)*

2. C *(1 mark)*

3.
$$
\begin{array}{r}
4\ 8^{7}\!1\!2 \\
-\ 2\ 3\ 7 \\
\hline
2\ 4\ 5
\end{array}
$$
(1 mark)

4. 17 is the only prime number less than 50 that can be made. *(1 mark)*

5. 4600 ÷ 10 = 460 *(1 mark)*
   4600 ÷ 100 = 46 *(1 mark)*

6. $10^3 - 10^2 - 10$
   = 1000 − 100 − 10 *(1 mark)*
   = 900 − 10 = 890 *(1 mark)*

7. Multiples of 3: 3, 6, 9, ⑫ 15, ...
   Multiples of 4: 4, 8, ⑫ 16, ...
   So they'll next get milk delivered on the same day 12 days after the 2nd June, which is the 14th June.
   (2 marks available — 1 mark for the correct method, 1 mark for the correct answer.)

Number: Test 4

1. C *(1 mark)*

2. B *(1 mark)*

3. Factors of 30 = 1, 2, 3, 5, 6, 10, 15, 30 *(1 mark)*

4. 45.79 = 45.8 (1 d.p.) *(1 mark)*

5. $\frac{4}{10} = \frac{2}{5}$ *(1 mark)*

6. $2^9 = 2^8 \times 2$ *(1 mark)*
   = 256 × 2 = 512 *(1 mark)*

7.
$$
\begin{array}{r}
5\ 2 \\
7\,\overline{)\,3\ 6^{1}4}
\end{array}
\text{ hours } (1\ mark)
$$

$$
\begin{array}{r}
3\ 5\ r\ 2 \\
6\,\overline{)\,2\ 1^{3}2}
\end{array}
\text{ hours}
$$
So he needs to work for 36 hours.
(2 marks available — 1 mark for the correct division, 1 mark for rounding up to 36.)

Number: Test 5

1. A *(1 mark)*

2. B *(1 mark)*

3. 1710 *(1 mark)*
   Twenty-nine thousand, seven hundred and fifty. *(1 mark)*

4. £6.75 + £3.50 = £10.25 *(1 mark)*

5. $\frac{5}{12} - \frac{1}{6} = \frac{5}{12} - \frac{2}{12} = \frac{3}{12} = \frac{1}{4}$
   (1 mark)

   $\frac{3}{8} \div \frac{2}{3} = \frac{3}{8} \times \frac{3}{2} = \frac{9}{16}$ *(1 mark)*

6.

(2 marks — 1 mark for each pair of factors.)
60 = 2 × 2 × 3 × 5 or $2^2 \times 3 \times 5$
(1 mark)

BONUS BRAINTEASER

Total cost = £8.75 + £6.75 + £3.50
= £19
Change = £20 − £19 = £1

Number: Test 6

1. B *(1 mark)*

2. A *(1 mark)*

3. 1 + 5 + 25 = 31 *(1 mark)*

4. Multiples of 3:
   3, 6, 9, 12, 15, 18, ㉑ 24, ...
   Multiples of 7: 7, 14, ㉑ 28, ...
   So the LCM of 3 and 7 is 21 *(1 mark)*

5. $2\frac{1}{3} = 2 + \frac{1}{3} = \frac{6}{3} + \frac{1}{3} = \frac{7}{3}$ *(1 mark)*

6. $\frac{18}{30} = \frac{3}{5} = 0.6 = 60\%$ *(1 mark)*

Answers

7. $\dfrac{101.2 \div 3.9}{5.1} \approx \dfrac{100 \div 4}{5} = \dfrac{25}{5} = 5$

(2 marks available — 1 mark for rounding all values correctly, 1 mark for the correct answer.)

8. $A = 12^2 = 144$ cm² *(1 mark)*

$S = \sqrt{2456} = 49.55804...$ cm

$= 49.6$ cm (1 d.p.) *(1 mark)*

Number: Test 7

1. C *(1 mark)*

2. A *(1 mark)*

3. $1085 - 978 = 107$ m *(1 mark)*

4. $A = 3.67 \times 100 = 367$

$B = 0.037 \times 1000 = 37$

$C = 0.307 \times 10\,000 = 3070$

Biggest: C *(1 mark)*

Smallest: B *(1 mark)*

5. $86\,668 = 87\,000$ to the nearest thousand *(1 mark)*

6. Zoe: $\dfrac{3}{8} = \dfrac{15}{40}$, Jim: $\dfrac{2}{5} = \dfrac{16}{40}$ *(1 mark)*

So Jim uses the most petrol. *(1 mark)*

7. $\dfrac{3^5}{3^3 \times 1^8} = \dfrac{3^5}{3^3 \times 1} = \dfrac{3^5}{3^3} = 3^{5-3}$ *(1 mark)*

$= 3^2 = 9$ *(1 mark)*

BONUS BRAINTEASER

Zoe uses $\dfrac{3}{8} \times 2 = \dfrac{6}{8} = \dfrac{3}{4}$ of a gallon of petrol to drive to and from work. This costs $\dfrac{3}{4} \times £8 = £6$.

Number: Test 8

1. B *(1 mark)*

2. B *(1 mark)*

3. 8, 16, 24, 32, 40 *(1 mark)*

4. $22 \times 14 = £308$

$134 \times 14 = £1876$

$1876 - 308 = £1568$

(2 marks available — 1 mark for a correct method, 1 mark for the correct answer.)

5. $\dfrac{4}{5} \times \dfrac{7}{8} = \dfrac{28}{40} = \dfrac{7}{10}$ *(1 mark)*

6. $12.25 + 0.512 = 12.726$ *(1 mark)*

7. $113 \div 3 = 37.666...$ and

$113 \div 7 = 16.142...$

113 is less than 120, ends in a 3 and doesn't divide by 3 or 7, so 113 is a prime number.

(2 marks for a full explanation, otherwise 1 mark for showing that 113 doesn't divide by 3 or 7.)

8. $(72 \div 60) \times 100 = 120\%$ *(1 mark)*

Number: Test 9

1. B *(1 mark)*

2. C *(1 mark)*

3. −14, −7, −1, 0, 3, 10 *(1 mark)*

4. $12 \times 75 = 900$p $= £9.00$

$10 \times 59 = 590$p $= £5.90$

$£9.00 + £5.90 = £14.90$

(2 marks available — 1 mark for finding the cost of 12 buckets and 10 spades, 1 mark for the correct answer.)

5. Factors of 28: 1, 2, 4, ⑦ 14, 28

Factors of 35 = 1, 5, ⑦ 35

So the HCF of 28 and 35 is 7.

(1 mark)

6. $\sqrt[3]{216} = 6$ *(1 mark)*

$\sqrt[4]{81} = 3$ *(1 mark)*

7. $21.4 \times 45.5 \approx 20 \times 50$ *(1 mark)*

$= 1000$ m² *(1 mark)*

BONUS BRAINTEASER

Area $= 21.4 \times 45.5 = 973.7$ m²

$973.7 \div 3 = 324.56666...$

So 325 packets of grass seed are needed.

Ratio, Proportion and Rates of Change: Test 1

1. A *(1 mark)*

2. B *(1 mark)*

3. $88 \div 11 = 8$

$2 \times 8 = 16$ seals *(1 mark)*

$12 \div 2 = 6$

$11 \times 6 = 66$ penguins *(1 mark)*

4. $30 \times 5 = 150$ selfies in 5 days *(1 mark)*

5. The map distance from the Theme Park to the Caravan Park is 6 cm. *(1 mark)*

Real-life distance $= 6 \times 3$ km

$= 18$ km *(1 mark)*

6. 10% of £40 $= £40 \div 10 = £4$,

so 20% of £40 $= £4 \times 2 = £8$

$£40 - £8 = £32$ *(1 mark)*

7. It took Andy 3 hours 30 mins $=$ 3.5 hours to complete the race. *(1 mark)*

22 km $\times$ 3.5 hours $= 77$ km *(1 mark)*

Ratio, Proportion and Rates of Change: Test 2

1. A *(1 mark)*

2. C *(1 mark)*

3. 1 jar: $£12.40 \div 8 = £1.55$ *(1 mark)*

5 jars: $£1.55 \times 5 = £7.75$ *(1 mark)*

4. Run: 5 miles ≈ 8 km $= 8000$ m

Swim: 7952 m

Cycle: 7.4 km $= 7400$ m

So she'll cycle the shortest distance.

(2 marks available — 1 mark for converting all distances into a common set of units, 1 mark for the correct answer.)

5. $6 \times 80 = 480$ cm *(1 mark)*

2.4 m $= 240$ cm *(1 mark)*

$240 \div 80 = 3$ cm *(1 mark)*

6. $800 \times 1.2 = 960$ g *(1 mark)*

BONUS BRAINTEASER

$7952 + 7400 = 15\,352$ m

$= 15.352$ km

Answers

Ratio, Proportion and Rates of Change: Test 3

1. A *(1 mark)*

2. C *(1 mark)*

3. $18 \div 4.5 = 4$ gallons *(1 mark)*

4. 19:48 = 7:48 pm *(1 mark)*
   2:05 pm = 14:05
   The next ferry leaves at 14:30, so
   James has to wait 25 mins. *(1 mark)*

5. Sm: £1.98 ÷ 1.5 kg = £1.32 per kg
   Med: £3.29 ÷ 2 kg = £1.645 per kg
   Lg: £6.32 ÷ 5 kg = £1.264 per kg
   So the large bag represents the best
   value for money.
   *(3 marks available — 1 mark for
   finding the price per kg for two of the
   bags, 1 mark for finding it for the third
   bag, 1 mark for the correct answer.)*

6. 2% interest = £260 × 0.02 = £5.20
   £5.20 × 3 = £15.60 *(1 mark)*
   £260 + £15.60 = £275.60 *(1 mark)*

Ratio, Proportion and Rates of Change: Test 4

1. B *(1 mark)*

2. C *(1 mark)*

3. 7:40 pm + 2 hours = 9:40 pm
   9:40 pm + 40 mins = 10:20 pm
   (1 mark)
   10:20 pm = 22:20 *(1 mark)*

4. 1 painter paints 9 ÷ 3 = 3 fences per
   day.
   So 5 painters would paint
   3 × 5 = 15 fences per day. *(1 mark)*

5. length on drawing = 4 cm *(1 mark)*
   4 × 50 = 200 cm
   200 cm = 2 m *(1 mark)*

6. Stan spent 3 hours cleaning and
   Laurel spent 3 + 2 = 5 hours cleaning.
   So the ratio of their hours is 3 : 5.
   (1 mark)
   The total number of parts: 3 + 5 = 8
   One part is: £56 ÷ 8 = £7 *(1 mark)*
   Laurel gets 7 × 5 = £35 *(1 mark)*

BONUS BRAINTEASER

$\frac{35}{56} = \frac{5}{8}$

Algebra: Test 1

1. B *(1 mark)*

2. A *(1 mark)*

3. $E = 12(20 - 8)$ *(1 mark)*
   $= 12 \times 12 = 144$ *(1 mark)*

4. $3s = 18$
   $s = 18 \div 3 = 6$ *(1 mark)*
   $u - 5 = 31$
   $u = 31 + 5 = 36$ *(1 mark)*

5.
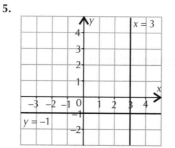

*(1 mark for both lines drawn
correctly.)*
They intersect at (3, –1). *(1 mark)*

6. Home to park = 30 minutes, park to
   beach = 1 hour, beach to home =
   1 hour *(1 mark for all three times)*
   Total time = 30 mins + 1 h + 1 h =
   2 hours and 30 minutes *(1 mark)*

Algebra: Test 2

1. C *(1 mark)*

2. B *(1 mark)*

3. $25 \times 3 - 7 = 75 - 7 = 68$ *(1 mark)*

4. 1, 4, 16, 64 *(1 mark)*
   50, 44, 38, 32 *(1 mark)*

5. $y = 5x + 6$
   *(2 marks available — 1 mark for the
   5x and 1 mark for the +6.)*

6. B *(1 mark)*

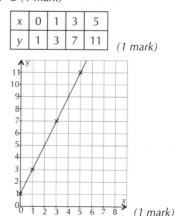

x	0	1	3	5
y	1	3	7	11

(1 mark)

(1 mark)

BONUS BRAINTEASER

Maria's score was 68 + 10 = 78.
Multiplying Alan's score by 4 gives:
25 × 4 = 100. 100 – 78 = 22, so to
complete the sentence, you need to
"subtract 22."

Algebra: Test 3

1. B *(1 mark)*

2. C *(1 mark)*

3.
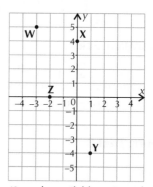

*(2 marks available — 2 marks for all
4 correct, otherwise 1 mark for 2 or 3
correct.)*

4. $D = \frac{C}{2} - 4$ *(1 mark)*

5. Each pattern has 2 squares more than
   the previous pattern. The 3rd pattern
   has 7 squares, so the 4th will have
   7 + 2 = 9 squares *(1 mark)* and the
   5th will have 9 + 2 = 11 squares
   (1 mark).

Answers

6. $t - 9 = 2 - 10t$
$t + 10t = 2 + 9$
$11t = 11$ *(1 mark)*
$t = 1$ *(1 mark)*

7. $5x + 6 = 32$
$5x = 26$
$5x - 6 = 26 - 6$
So $5x - 6 = 20$ *(1 mark)*

Algebra: Test 4

1. B *(1 mark)*

2. B *(1 mark)*

3. $8 \times 1 - 12 = 8 - 12 = -4$ *(1 mark)*
$8 \times 10 - 12 = 80 - 12 = 68$ *(1 mark)*

4. $C = 5 + n$ *(1 mark)*

5. 20 g *(1 mark)*
40 g would cost 30p *(1 mark)*,
so 40 g × 10 = 400 g would cost
30p × 10 = 300p = £3 *(1 mark)*

6. To find each term, add 4 to the previous term, so the nth term contains $4n$. When $n = 1$, $4n = 4$, and to get from 4 to –9, subtract 13. So the nth term is $4n - 13$.
(2 marks available — 2 marks for the correct answer, otherwise 1 mark for 4n.)

BONUS BRAINTEASER
Use your formula for the nth term:
$4n - 13 = 31$
$4n = 44$, $n = 11$

Algebra: Test 5

1. B *(1 mark)*

2. C *(1 mark)*

3. $E = 2.5 \times 10 \times 4 = 25 \times 4 = 100$ *(1 mark)*

4. $p + 10 = -2$
$p = -2 - 10 = -12$ *(1 mark)*

5. $50 - 3 \times 10 = 50 - 30 = 20$ *(1 mark)*

6. $2(2a + 1) + a(4 + a) + 3(3 + 3a)$
$= 4a + 2 + 4a + a^2 + 9 + 9a$ *(1 mark)*
$= a^2 + 17a + 11$ *(1 mark)*

7.

x	0	1	2	3
y	–5	–3	–1	1

(1 mark)

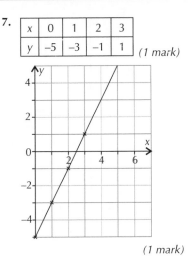

(1 mark)

The graph crosses the x-axis at $(2.5, 0)$ *(1 mark)*.

Geometry and Measures: Test 1

1. A *(1 mark)*

2. C *(1 mark)*

3. Volume = $6.2 \times 8 \times 3.1$
$= 153.76$ cm^3 *(1 mark)*

4. Area = $12 \times 7 = 84$ cm^2 *(1 mark)*

5. $x = 180° - 75° - 75° = 30°$
(2 marks available — 1 mark for a correct method, 1 mark for the correct answer.)

6. Radius = $1.5 \div 2 = 0.75$ m *(1 mark)*
Area = $\pi \times 0.75^2 = 1.7671...$
$= 1.77$ m^2 (2 d.p.) *(1 mark)*

7. E.g.

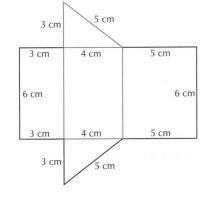

(2 marks available — 1 mark for drawing the net correctly, 1 mark for labelling it correctly.)

Geometry and Measures: Test 2

1. C *(1 mark)*

2. B *(1 mark)*

3. Perimeter = $30 + 45 + 30 + 45$
$= 150$ cm *(1 mark)*
Perimeter = $30 + 30 + 45$
$+ 30 + 30 + 45$ *(1 mark)*
$= 210$ cm *(1 mark)*

4. $p = 180° - 90° - 34° = 56°$ *(1 mark)*

5.

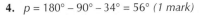
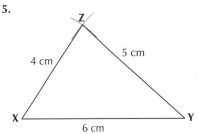

(2 marks available — 1 mark for the correct construction marks, 1 mark for a correctly drawn shape.)

6. Surface area = $2(4 \times 2) + 2(4 \times 6)$
$+ 2(2 \times 6)$ *(1 mark)*
$= 16 + 48 + 24 = 88$ cm^2 *(1 mark)*

BONUS BRAINTEASER

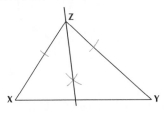

Geometry and Measures: Test 3

1. C *(1 mark)*

2. A *(1 mark)*

Answers

Answers

3.

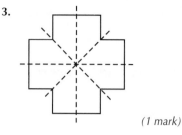

(1 mark)

4. Width = 28 ÷ 8 = 3.5 m *(1 mark)*

5. A cross should be drawn at (5, 2).
(1 mark)

90° *(1 mark)*

6. 12 × 15 = 180 cm³ *(1 mark)*

7. Sum of the interior angles of a
pentagon: 180 × (5 − 2) = 540°
(1 mark)
w = 540 − 66 − 192 − 78 − 94
(1 mark) = 110° *(1 mark)*

Geometry and Measures: Test 4

1. C *(1 mark)*

2. A *(1 mark)*

3.

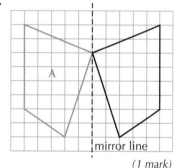

mirror line

(1 mark)

4. One missing side will be 9 cm, so the
third side = 24 − 9 − 9 = 6 cm.
(1 mark for both correct)

5.

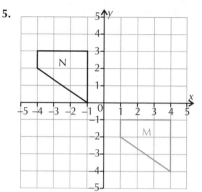

*(2 marks available — 1 mark for the
correct horizontal translation, 1 mark
for the correct vertical translation.)*

6. a = 27° *(1 mark)*
b = 180 − 27 = 153° *(1 mark)*

7.

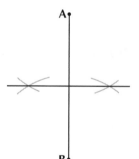

*(2 marks available — 1 mark for
correctly drawn construction arcs,
1 mark for a correct and accurate
perpendicular bisector.)*

Geometry and Measures: Test 5

1. C *(1 mark)*

2. B *(1 mark)*

3. 12 *(1 mark)*
8 *(1 mark)*

4. C and G *(1 mark)*
E *(1 mark)*

5. Area = ½ × 4 × 2.5 = 5 m² *(1 mark)*
Volume = 5 × 5 = 25 m³ *(1 mark)*

6. 2 *(1 mark)*
(0, 4) *(1 mark)*

BONUS BRAINTEASER

(3, 3), (9, 3) and (3, 6)

Geometry and Measures: Test 6

1. A *(1 mark)*

2. C *(1 mark)*

3. 10 *(1 mark)*; 10 *(1 mark)*

4. m = 360 − 81 − 48 − 103 = 128°
(1 mark)
n = 360 − 55 − 90 − 79 = 136°
(1 mark)

5. Area of rectangle = 8 × 12 = 96 cm²
Area of triangle = ½ × 8 × 6
= 24 cm²
Total area = 96 + 24 = 120 cm²
*(2 marks available for the correct
answer, otherwise 1 mark for correctly
finding the area of the rectangle or
the triangle.)*

6. Area of circle = π × 7²
= 153.9380... cm²
Area of square = 5 × 5 = 25 cm²
Area of plastic = 153.9380... − 25
= 128.9380... = 128.94 cm² (2 d.p.)
*(2 marks available — 1 mark for
finding the area of the circle, 1 mark
for the correct answer.)*

Geometry and Measures: Test 7

1. B *(1 mark)*

2. A *(1 mark)*

3.

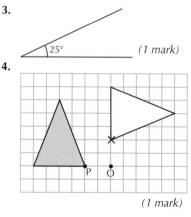

(1 mark)

4.

(1 mark)

5. u = 54° *(1 mark)*
v = 180 − 62 = 118° *(1 mark)*
w = 180 − 62 − 54 = 64° *(1 mark)*

Answers

6.

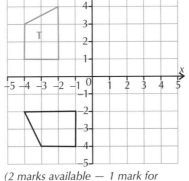

(1 mark)

7. $m = 360 \div 12 = 30°$ *(1 mark)*
$n = 180 - 30 = 150°$ *(1 mark)*

Geometry and Measures: Test 8

1. C *(1 mark)*

2. B *(1 mark)*

3. E.g.

	3 cm	
2 cm		2 cm

2 cm		2 cm	3 cm
5 cm			5 cm
2 cm		2 cm	3 cm

2 cm		2 cm
	3 cm	

(2 marks available — 1 mark for drawing the net correctly, 1 mark for labelling it correctly.)

4. $a = 142°$ *(1 mark)*
$b = 180 - 142 = 38°$ *(1 mark)*

5. Circumference $= 1.4 \times 2 \times \pi$
$= 8.7964... = 8.80$ m (2 d.p.)
(2 marks available — 1 mark for using the correct formula, 1 mark for the correct answer.)

6.

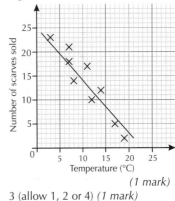

(2 marks available — 1 mark for correctly drawn construction arcs, 1 mark for a correct and accurate angle bisector.)

BONUS BRAINTEASER
Surface area
$= 2(3 \times 2) + 2(3 \times 5) + 2(2 \times 5)$
$= 12 + 30 + 20 = 62$ cm²
Volume $= 2 \times 3 \times 5 = 30$ cm³

Geometry and Measures: Test 9

1. C *(1 mark)*

2. A *(1 mark)*

3. $\begin{pmatrix} 6 \\ -2 \end{pmatrix}$ *(1 mark)*

$\begin{pmatrix} -5 \\ -2 \end{pmatrix}$ *(1 mark)*

4. $s = (180 - 108) \div 2 = 36°$ *(1 mark)*
$t = 180 - 36 = 144°$ *(1 mark)*

5.

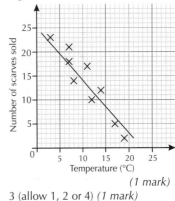

(2 marks available — 1 mark for shape rotated 90° anticlockwise, 1 mark for correct position on grid.)

6. Cross-sectional area $= \pi \times 4.2^2$
$= 55.4176... = 55.42$ cm² (2 d.p.)
(1 mark)
Volume $= 55.4176... \times 12.8$
$= 709.3464... = 709.35$ cm³ (2 d.p.)
(1 mark)

Probability and Statistics: Test 1

1. A *(1 mark)*

2. C *(1 mark)*

3. $4 \times 2 = 8$ *(1 mark)*

(1 mark)
$7 + 8 + 5 + 2 = 22$ *(1 mark)*

4. $8 - 3 = 5$ (1 mark)
7 *(1 mark)*

5. continuous *(1 mark)*

6. E.g.

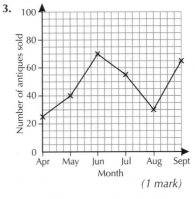

(1 mark)
3 (allow 1, 2 or 4) *(1 mark)*

Probability and Statistics: Test 2

1. C *(1 mark)*

2. A *(1 mark)*

3.

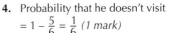

(1 mark)

4. Probability that he doesn't visit
$= 1 - \frac{5}{6} = \frac{1}{6}$ *(1 mark)*

Answers

Answers

5. $18 + 21 + 22 + 17 + 19 = 97$
Mean = $97 \div 5 = 19.4$ °C *(1 mark)*

6. HR, HB, HG, HY,
TR, TB, TG, TY *(1 mark)*

Probability of HB = $\frac{1}{8}$ *(1 mark)*

Probability of TR or TY = $\frac{2}{8} = \frac{1}{4}$
(1 mark)

7. Total: $15 + 8 + 5 + 2 = 30$
Multiplier = $360 \div 30 = 12$
Dog: $15 \times 12 = 180°$
Cat: $8 \times 12 = 96°$
Rabbit: $5 \times 12 = 60°$
Other: $2 \times 12 = 24°$
*(2 marks for all 4 angles correct,
otherwise 1 mark for working out
correct multiplier.)*

Probability and Statistics: Test 3

1. C *(1 mark)*

2. B *(1 mark)*

3. Probability of picking an E = $\frac{2}{6} = \frac{1}{3}$
(1 mark)

Probability of picking a vowel
= $\frac{4}{6} = \frac{2}{3}$ *(1 mark)*

4. 11 *(1 mark)*

$10 + 13 = 23$ *(1 mark)*

5. Put the data in order: 94, 99, 101,
108, 115, 122, 125
Median = 4th value = 108 minutes
*(2 marks available — 1 mark for
putting the data in order, 1 mark for
the correct answer.)*

6.

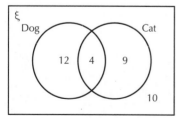

*(2 marks for all four values in the
correct places, otherwise 1 mark for
two or three values in the correct
place.)*

BONUS BRAINTEASER

There are $12 + 4 + 9 + 10 = 35$
teenagers in total. 4 of them
have a dog and a cat, so the
probability that a randomly selected
student has a dog and a cat is $\frac{4}{35}$.

Probability and Statistics: Test 4

1. B *(1 mark)*

2. C *(1 mark)*

3. $16 + 14 + 13 + 11 + 10 = 64$
(1 mark)

4. G = {3, 6, 9, 12} *(1 mark)*
F or G = {2, 3, 4, 6, 8, 9, 10, 12}
(1 mark)
n(F) = 6 *(1 mark)*

5. $11 \times 3 = 33$
$33 - 15 - 8 = 10$ *(1 mark)*

6. Total frequency: 40
Number of cars × frequency:
0, 12, 28, 18, 12 (total = 70)
*(2 marks for all values correct,
otherwise 1 mark for two or three
values correct.)*

Mean = $70 \div 40 = 1.75$ cars
(1 mark)

M1XP31